"You never know when one kind act or one word of encouragement will change a life forever."

- David L. Burrier

Presented to:

_____

From:

_____

Date:

_____

"Taking back family reading time since 2018!"

Author Dedication

I dedicate this book to my brother, Daniel, who continues to inspire me since his life-changing stroke at the age of 49. Over the years, people who know Dan have asked me, "How is your disabled brother doing?" My response has always been the same, "I don't have a disabled brother, but I do have a differently-abled brother."

Dan's stroke resulted in a permanent condition called Expressive Aphasia, impacting his ability to speak, write, read, and walk. As a result, Dan was left paralyzed on his right side and he has limited eyesight. My brother is not disabled, but he is differently-abled. People love being around Dan because he is kind, smart, compassionate, and sensitive to others that are also physically challenged.

I love you so much, brother Dan!

To God be the Glory!

- David L. Burrier

The "Just for You" Pet Shop!

Written by David L. Burrier
Edited by Craig Biss
Illustrated by Candace Camling

Alex is a short, red-haired, freckle-faced nine-year-old boy. Early in his life, Alex experienced a rare disease that changed his life forever. As a result of the illness, his speech is sluggish and to balance his steps, he walks with crutches. Make no mistake about it, though, Alex is not disabled.

ALEX IS DIFFERENTLY-ABLED!

Alex struggled to keep up with the other boys and girls on his way to school. Hurrying with his crutches was difficult and the other children ran past him.

During the school day, the other kids teased him, saying things like, "Alex is a slowpoke!", "Alex will never be normal!" and "Alex stutters when he reads!" Every day, Alex chose to smile even though some of the other children at school picked on him. Their comments stung, but Alex chose to find happiness despite what others said about him.

When the classroom bell rang and the school day was over, there was always one thing that brought a smile to Alex's face. He would gather his books and head over to his favorite place in town, the "Just for You" Pet Shop on Main Street. The pet shop was only a couple blocks away and the weather outside was beautiful.

The owner usually had a special display in the front window featuring one or more of the many pets he had to offer for adoption. Alex would play with the pets and he would dream of adopting one of his own someday.

Most of the pets up for adoption were older rescue animals and Alex took great joy in playing with them. Today at the "Just for You" Pet Shop, Alex was surprised to see a litter of 12 new puppies.

The sign in the window read, "Adopt a puppy today! Only $25! JUST FOR YOU!"

Alex entered the shop and made his way to the adoption kennel where the new puppies were frolicking.

The puppies were full of life and energy! As Alex watched them play, he noticed one of the puppies was different from the others. The puppy was considerably smaller than the rest, seemed to

have a slight limp, and had sad, droopy eyes. The little puppy stumbled around the kennel struggling to keep up with the other puppies.

While the other puppies played on the far side of the kennel, the differently-abled puppy moved closer to Alex. Alex grinned widely and stood at the side of the kennel watching.

Walking home from school, other children noticed the sign in the pet shop window, too. They did not notice Alex standing there or even acknowledge him by saying, "hello". As the children moved in closer to see the puppies in the kennel, they noticed the differently-abled puppy and made comments like, "Look at that puppy!", "He is a slowpoke!", "That puppy will never be normal!", and "That puppy stumbles when he walks!"

Alex felt the sadness building up inside of him for the little puppy and tried to ignore the comments

made by the children. Hearing the other children laugh and tease about the puppy brought back to Alex memories of what the children said to him while he was at school.

Alex considered the remarks the children made toward the puppy. Even so, he noticed that the puppy continued to wag his tail and be happy. Alex, too, would choose to be happy regardless of what was said about him!

The owner of the pet shop was a seemingly tall man who had a friendly voice and large shoulders.

The owner watched from behind the counter, occasionally stood to greet new customers, and was working at his computer. From behind the counter, he heard how the children were behaving.

In a firm, but polite way, he told the other children that perhaps it was time that they go home; after all, their parents were probably wondering why they were not home from school yet.

"Let's get out of here!" the oldest and tallest kid bristled.

"Yeah, this place is boring anyway!" replied another kid.

The children left the shop hastily. The owner pointed at Alex and said that he was more than welcome to stay if he wanted. As Alex leaned closer to the kennel, the differently-abled puppy moved closer to Alex, sat up, and licked the side of Alex's face. Alex was delighted and laughed as the puppy with the sad, droopy eyes wagged his tail.

Alex was enjoying his visit so much that an hour of time had passed before he knew it. He needed to get home for dinner.

During the evening, Alex smiled as he recalled his visit to the pet shop. He could not wait to stop by the pet shop when he walked home from school the next day. It was difficult to fall asleep that night as Alex dreamed of seeing the puppy again.

The next day at school, Alex drew a picture of the puppy and showed it to his best friend, Jacob. Jacob had been Alex's friend for as long as he could remember, but Jacob was often out of school because

8

he had been battling an illness on and off for the last two years. The illness caused Jacob to miss a lot of school days.

When Jacob was able to come to school, Alex was excited to share what Jacob had missed and he especially wanted to share the exciting news of the puppy at the "Just for You" Pet Shop.

Jacob shared Alex's excitement for the puppy and he and Alex made plans to visit the puppy after school. Jacob, like Alex, was differently-abled, as well, and offered Alex a ride on his wheelchair scooter so they could get to the pet shop faster.

Counting down the last few minutes of the school day, Alex finally heard the classroom bell ring. He and Jacob gathered their books and made their way to the pet shop as planned. Alex jumped on the back of Jacob's scooter and away they went.

"Hold on tight," exclaimed Jacob.

They arrived just in time to see all the puppies lining up to be fed milk from bottles that were hanging on the kennel.

The puppies eagerly found their bottles except for the differently-abled puppy. His sad, droopy eyes watched as the other puppies enjoyed their meal. The differently-abled puppy struggled to find a place to drink as the other larger puppies pushed him aside.

Alex noticed that two puppies were missing and discovered that both had been adopted earlier in the day. There were still 10 puppies left. Alex and Jacob put their faces up to the kennel just as Alex had done the previous day. Within seconds, the differently-abled puppy came over and licked their faces. Alex declared that this puppy be named "Happy" because he chose to be happy!

Jacob giggled and Alex felt an overwhelming joy knowing that showing kindness towards others, even a differently-abled puppy, truly made a difference in the world. Alex remembered how kind Jacob was to him when no one else showed they cared. It had made a difference in Alex's life.

"I think this puppy was made just for you!" Jacob said to Alex.

"Yes!" Alex responded eagerly, "And I think I was made for him, too!"

Jacob pointed to the sign about adopting a puppy that read "$25 to adopt" and mentioned to Alex that now there were only 10 puppies left. Alex's heart dropped in his chest, realizing that not only was he lacking $25, but before he could earn the money, someone could come along and adopt

Happy! He groaned as he considered never being able to see Happy again.

At dinner that night, Alex told his mother and father about the puppies at the "Just for You" Pet Shop. He explained that the store owner only wanted $25 to adopt one. Alex's parents listened and then lovingly responded as most parents do. "Honey," Alex's mother replied, "we just do not have the money to spare on a puppy right now."

"You have to remember, Alex," said his father, "that

vaccination shots and supplies like a kennel, food, and toys are additional costs when you have a pet."

After further discussion, Alex's mother made a deal with him. Alex could adopt a puppy if he could come up with the adoption money, plus money for the additional expenses, and, if Alex promised to take care of the puppy.

Alex was overjoyed at the thought of "maybe" getting a puppy in the future; that is, if he could come up with the money! His father quickly changed the subject of getting a new pet and they discussed other things at the table. As soon as

13

dinner was finished, however, Alex called Jacob on the phone to share the exciting news.

On the phone that night, Jacob told Alex how excited he was for him but reminded Alex that $25, plus the extra money needed, was still a lot of money! Jacob also cautioned that Happy may be adopted sooner than later. That was all true, but Alex was going to stay positive and motivated to be able to adopt Happy!

After school each day, Alex would stop by the pet shop to visit his little puppy friend, Happy. Jacob could not always come with Alex so Alex would let

Jacob know the number of puppies that remained for adoption. After several visits, Alex noticed that the number of puppies left was decreasing quickly. One afternoon, he arrived to discover that Happy was the only puppy left at the pet shop!

Alex walked toward the kennel slowly. Happy stood there wagging his tail waiting for Alex to come closer. Alex paused as he heard the owner of the pet shop beckon him to come over to the counter. Alex

had never spoken to the owner before and wondered what he could want with him.

"Hello, young man," said the owner. "My name is Patrick, but you can call me Pat."

Pat and Alex made small talk about the weather, favorite foods, and their upcoming weekend plans, then Pat finally asked Alex about his reason for coming by the pet shop each day.

"I noticed," said Pat, "that you come in here every day and always play with the same puppy. Why is that?"

"Well," responded Alex, "I am saving my money from lunch each day so I can adopt this puppy. I have already named him, Happy."

"That puppy?" Pat pointed to the adoption kennel. "I don't think you want that puppy," said Pat. "He is small, walks with a limp, and has sad, droopy eyes."

At this description, Alex straightened up and

waited patiently for his chance to respond to Pat's comments. When he had an opportunity, Alex told Pat that every day was a struggle for him at school because he, Alex, was differently-abled.

Alex explained to Pat that the very same things people said about this puppy in the pet shop were the same things that people often said about him at school.

"Pat," Alex went on to explain, "my best friend, Jacob, is also differently-abled. Kindness and compassion shown to both Jacob and me makes all the difference in the world. I feel the same kindness and compassion towards this little puppy. That is why I want to adopt him."

Pat's heart warmed towards Alex. The very things that caused most people to turn away from the puppy yet to be adopted were the same things that made Alex want the puppy!

As he visited with Pat, Alex noticed the clock on the wall read 5 o'clock, he realized that it was close to dinner time, and told Pat that he needed to go. Pat thanked Alex for chatting with him and waved as Alex moved closer to the exit of the store.

"Oh, wait!" gestured Pat, "Will you come by the shop tomorrow?"

"You can count on it!" replied Alex, "I will see you tomorrow!"

Alex walked home thinking about his conversation with Pat. He really, really wanted to adopt Happy and was glad that he had shared his thoughts with Pat. He hoped that Happy would still be there when he arrived after school tomorrow!

As he approached his house, he caught the aroma of dinner wafting through the screen door. The smell of meat loaf and potato salad made him realize that he was hungry!

"Hi, mom!" he said with a smile. "I know what's for dinner... meat loaf!"

The next day at school dragged on for what seemed like forever. Alex sat there barely able to concentrate on his school work.

Thankfully, Jacob was back and Alex shared with him the conversation he had with Pat, the pet shop owner.

Jacob, who had been gone from school, was still not feeling the best, but he was delighted to see how ecstatic his best friend, Alex, was about the puppy. Alex told Jacob that he had been skipping dessert at the cafeteria every day and was saving a dollar out of his $4 lunch money to adopt Happy. All he needed was a couple more weeks and he would have enough money.

The classroom bell rang at the end of the day and was like music to the boys' ears. It was not that they did not enjoy school, but they had a more important plan! It was finally time to go see Happy at the "Just for You" Pet Shop.

Jacob offered to give Alex a ride on his wheelchair scooter so they could get to the pet shop without delay. Jacob even allowed Alex to drive the scooter this time. Jacob held the crutches for Alex and Jacob swung his legs off the back of the scooter.

As they sped down the street towards the pet shop, they were happily talking about the puppy, laughing, and enjoying the warm breeze. Plus, Alex had never driven anything before, so this was an unexpected surprise.

The pet shop came into view. Alex hopped off the wheelchair scooter, grabbed his crutches and hurried toward the pet shop window with Jacob following in his wheelchair scooter. Alex eagerly investigated the window, searching for Happy. "Happy is gone!" groaned Alex.

As they entered the pet shop, they saw Pat, the owner, sitting behind the counter going through a large stack of mail. Alex quickly scanned the store, hurrying through the aisles while trying not to knock over any merchandise with his crutches.

As he neared the kennel, he saw that it was empty and the "Adopt a Puppy Today" sign was gone! Alex hung his head trying to hold back his tears. Jacob moved a little closer. He, too, hung his head knowing that his friend was in deep pain.

Pat lifted his head from his mail stack and called out to Alex.

"Hey, Alex! It is nice to see you today!"

Alex lifted his chin and tried to smile even though he could barely breathe from his sorrow. He didn't know what to say. Every night before going to bed, he had prayed that one day, Happy, would be his puppy. Reality was starting to feel like a real kick in the teeth.

Jacob came closer to Alex. He quietly reminded Alex that if Happy was adopted, then another family was probably loving on him right now. Alex thought about that and knew that he desperately wanted Happy to be his puppy, but even more than that, he wanted Happy to be "happy".

Pat sat patiently, observing the love, empathy and compassion of Alex's friend, Jacob. A tear slowly formed in Pat's eye and rolled down his cheek before falling onto the counter.

Alex drew closer to the counter and asked Pat about the family that had adopted the last puppy. "Did they look kind?" and "Were they showing compassion for the little sad, droopy-eyed puppy?" Alex inquired.

Pat told Alex that it had been hard to find the perfect home for the puppy because no one seemed to want him. Of all the puppies to adopt, this little puppy was the last one that anyone would ever consider adopting. Pat continued to say that after

weeks of trying, the right person had finally come to adopt the puppy.

In answer to Alex's questions, Pat said, "The puppy was wagging his tail and was very excited to be adopted."

Alex thought about the puppy, he smiled, overcame his sorrow, and pulled $23 from his pocket.

"I would like to buy Happy a couple of gifts. Can you please make sure they get to his new owner?" asked Alex.

Pat smiled from ear to ear. Not only had Alex been saving money to adopt Happy, he was even willing to spend the money on gifts for the little guy that was not even his. Alex just wanted to bless the new owner.

Alex and Jacob browsed around the pet shop and filled the counter with $23 worth of chew toys,

treats, and a shiny new blue collar with a silver-plated tag that read, "Best Dog Ever" etched into the surface.

"Do you think Happy will like his new stuff?" asked Alex.

"I know he will love it!" replied Pat, winking at Jacob.

The boys stood there. They could hear a thump, thump, thumping sound coming from behind the counter. Pat had already rung up all the items on the counter and was putting them in a bag. The total cost of the items was $22.75. Pat handed Alex a quarter as his change and Alex placed it in his pocket.

Again, the boys could hear a noise coming from behind the counter which this time sounded like a little bark! Jacob leaned forward in his wheelchair scooter trying to determine what was making the noises behind the counter.

"What's behind the counter, Pat?" Alex asked.

"Well," said Pat, "It's a special gift for you! I have been watching you for weeks as you have come to the pet shop and played with one little sad, droopy-eyed puppy who has a limp and can barely move around. You have exhibited a kindness and compassion towards that little puppy that I don't see very often. And because of that, I have a gift for you."

Alex patiently watched as Pat lifted a kennel from behind the counter. They had know idea what was inside of the kennel. To their amazement and delight, there sat Happy wagging his tail inside the kennel.

"Happy!" Alex shouted. "I thought you said he had a new owner, Pat?"

"I did!" declared Pat. "That new owner is you, Alex!"

Pat placed the kennel on the counter. Jacob was speechless and Alex began fumbling for words to say that could explain his joy.

"I don't have $25, Pat!" Alex responded as his face dropped.

Pat stood there and smiled while Alex continued to speak.

"I just spent all my money on chew toys, treats, and a new collar!" exclaimed Alex.

Pat slowly stood up. He was as tall as ever but then bent over as his stature diminished. Alex and Jacob were truly baffled by Pat's physical size. What was going on?

Pat moved from behind the counter. He held onto the edge of the counter with his right hand. He moved back and motioned for Alex to come and look behind the counter. There stood a large wooden stool where Pat had been sitting.

Alex looked to Pat. He noticed that Pat's left hand held a cane onto which he leaned. It suddenly occurred to Alex that Pat was differently-abled, too! Sitting behind the pet shop counter had allowed Pat to seem tall, but he was actually quite short and walked with a limp.

Alex and Jacob realized the bond they had with Pat. Their bond was not because they were differently-abled, but because they cared about others. Pat pulled the sign out from behind the counter that read, "Adopt a puppy today!" and with a red marker made a few quick changes and additions to the sign. The sign now read:

ADOPT A PUPPY TODAY

**ONLY 25 CENTS
KENNEL INCLUDED
JUST FOR YOU**

Realizing he had just the right amount of money, Alex pulled the quarter from his pocket and placed it in Pat's hand. Happy let out an excited bark!

"Congratulations, Alex, this puppy is just for you!" said Pat with tears in his eyes.

The news of what happened that day at the pet shop spread throughout the town. Before long, the local and national newspapers had picked up the story and in no time, people from near and far came to visit the "Just for You" Pet Shop. Every morning there is a line waiting to get into the store.

Now Pat never tries to hide being differently-abled. He has also put a new sign in his shop directly above the counter that reads, "Kindness, compassion, and loving others makes a big difference!"

Pat, with the help of Alex and Jacob, has started a new pet adoption center where differently-abled animals can find loving homes. They have already successfully helped 10 pets find new homes.

Jacob has fully recovered from his illness and his doctors are optimistic about his most recent test results. When Jacob's parents heard about Alex and his new puppy, they surprised Jacob on Christmas morning with a puppy of his own. Jacob happily named him, Jolly.

Alex plays with Happy every day and is amazed to see how much he is growing. Happy is one confident little guy and he brings much joy to Alex's life. Jacob comes over frequently to play with Happy and sometimes he brings Jolly over, too.

The boys are reminded often, through the events of adopting Happy, that a single act of kindness, compassion, and love has changed their lives forever.

The "Just for You" Pet Shop
What can it teach our children?

1. What did you learn from this book?
2. Why do you think other children made fun of Alex?
3. How do you think that made Alex feel?
4. Have you ever seen kids (or adults) do that to others?
5. What did you do when you saw them doing that?
6. Have you ever had that happen to you?
7. If so, how did that make you feel?
8. What was Alex's best friend's name?
9. Why do you think they were friends?
10. Did Alex's friend Jacob make fun of him?
11. Why do you think Jacob didn't make fun of Alex?
12. Why did Alex choose to be happy?
13. Why did Alex want to adopt the puppy that nobody else wanted?
14. What do you think differently-abled means?
15. Have you ever met anyone differently-abled?
16. Do you have any differently-abled friends?
17. If so, what makes them different?
18. Why do you think Alex named the puppy Happy?
19. Why didn't anyone else want to adopt Happy?
20. What can you do when you experience someone being made fun of or picked on for being differently-abled?

*An adult supplemental discussion group questionnaire is available in PDF for download at www.justforyoubook.com

About the Author

David L. Burrier is a follower of Jesus, author, award winning poet, motivational speaker, singer, songwriter, producer, master storyteller, and hope coach. His mission in life is to be a source of inspiration, so that whoever he encounters will walk away with a renewed sense of mission and a purpose in life. David's life is guided by the philosophical quote,

"If you assume that every person you meet is fighting a battle you know nothing about, or is hurting in some way, you will be right 99% of the time. So just be kind and seek to lift their spirit. Give them hope to live another day."

Read David's daily messages of hope on IBTM Facebook page at www.facebook.com/ivebeenthereministries

Send all Facebook friend requests to David at www.facebook.com/david.burrier.56

Contact David directly through email at imfullofhope@hotmail.com

For more information about The "Just for You" Pet Shop book or to schedule David as your speaker, please visit www.justforyoubook.com

Learn more about David at www.davidlburrier.com or www.stringthingbook.com

Look for additional books in the Burrie' Children's Book Series coming soon at www. burrierbooks.com

Now available on Amazon from

The Ballerina and the Bear Publishing!

Featuring Author David L. Burrier

Featuring Author Marc Cota-Robles

Featuring Author Craig Biss

Made in the USA
Columbia, SC
15 February 2022

55836805R00026